KEEP YOUNG AND BEAUTIFUL

KEEP YOUNG AND BEAUTIFUL

Barbara Cartland
&
Elinor Glyn

Duckworth

First published in 1982 by
Gerald Duckworth and Company Ltd.,
The Old Piano Factory,
43 Gloucester Crescent, London N.W.1.

Original version of main text by Elinor Glyn
first published (as 'The Wrinkle Book') in 1927

ISBN 0 7156 1496 7

British Library Cataloguing in Publication Data

Glyn, Elinor
  Keep young and beautiful
  1. Beauty culture
  I. Title   II. Cartland, Barbara
  646.7'2'088042   TT957

  ISBN 0-7156-1496-7

Photoset by E.B. Photosetting Ltd., Speke, Liverpool
and printed by A. Wheaton & Co. Ltd., Exeter

Contents

Preface

Elinor Glyn was the most exciting, most controversial figure of my youth. Her novels, which were considered wildly improper, were spoken of with bated breath, and her life story lost nothing in the telling.

Half French, she refused to marry an ebullient peer with a walrus moustache, the Duke of Newcastle, and a millionaire who was vulgar and common, before she accepted Clayton Glyn, a wealthy country gentleman.

On their honeymoon, Clayton hired a swimming bath so that she could swim naked with her long red hair trailing behind her.

It was his last romantic gesture.

In Venice he insisted on her lady's maid accompanying them in their gondola at night, and Elinor began to ache for a dream lover. Her yearnings for love, her frustration and her passionate nature were all revealed when, from the proceeds of her first novel, she bought a tiger skin.

Clayton came into the room to find his wife reclining on the floor on the tiger, stroking its skin, quivering with emotion, and staring at him with dark smouldering eyes.

Little wonder that her novel *Three Weeks* exploded like a bomb on an astonished public. A rhyme added to her reputation as a scarlet woman:

> Would you like to sin
> With Elinor Glyn
> On a tiger skin?
> Or would you prefer
> To err with her
> On some other fur?

Clayton's illness and wild extravagance caused his financial collapse, and Elinor was forced to support him and their family by writing. No one could have done so more graciously.

The great love of her life was the Marquess Curzon of Kedleston, whom she met in 1908. He was a cold, aloof intellectual, a dedicated statesman – ambitious, egotistical and, like Elinor, very class-conscious.

She wrote to him as follows, with all the romantic intensity of one of her heroines:

> 'I love you, not *because* of your noble head and your greatness, not in *spite* of your selfishness, but just because I do, and you are you, for me the sun, moon and stars and the end of time.'

Elinor did many unpredictable things.

She visited Russia, wrote her Russian novel *His Hour* and read it aloud to the whole court.

Humiliated by her husband borrowing £1,000 from a friend which he had no intention of repaying, she wrote *The Reason Why*, a novel of 90,000 words, in exactly three weeks.

In 1914, amazingly, she became a war correspondent, risking her life by visiting the battle areas. She investigated stories of German atrocities of torture and rape, and she stayed in Paris when everyone she knew had fled during the bombardment.

One day in 1916, after eight and a half years of a rapturous, passionate love affair, she suddenly read, without warning, a notice in *The Times* of Curzon's engagement to another woman.

She never saw or wrote to Curzon again. As proudly as her ancestors had faced the guillotine, she burnt his letters, of which there were five hundred.

In Hollywood, Elinor Glyn disliked the phrase 'sex appeal' and invented the word 'It' to describe 'a strange magnetism which attracts both sexes'.

'It' was what she had all her life.

When I met Elinor Glyn at the Ritz in the early thirties, she was no longer in her first youth, but she was still very beautiful. She carried herself erect, like a queen. She looked at people imperiously, and her brilliant green eyes, red hair and magnificent white skin were breathtaking.

The secret of her beauty was once described by Beverley Nichols as follows:

> 'Elinor Glyn does not loll about on tiger skins, nor on anything else. She sits bolt upright on a chair. Hence she has the shoulders of a young girl, although she is a grandmother. She does not drink liquors. She drinks water – lots of it. Discipline, discipline, discipline – that is the rhythm of Elinor Glyn's life. Mental discipline as well as physical.'

In *Keep Young and Beautiful*, first published, under another title, in 1927, Elinor Glyn describes the discipline of facial exercises she devised to help women keep their looks. Though written more than fifty years ago, it is still one of the best books ever written on the subject.

The facial exercises Elinor proposes are all very simple, *because they follow true physiological principles*. They take very little time to perform – as little as five minutes a day – and if practised regularly will produce the most excellent results, I can assure you.

At the end I have added some recommendations of my own, based on new scientific facts not known in Elinor's day. As they are in harmony with her ideas, I know she would have approved of them.

None of us wants to live for ever. What we want is to enjoy every day and every moment while we are alive, and the way to do so is to 'live young'. This is the formula of beauty and of happiness! This book will help you on the way to both!

Barbara Cartland

Chapter One

GIVE LOVE

Men have combed the world for gold,
Olympian Goddesses of old sought love.
What do you seek – a happy life?
Or one of constant, endless strife,
To be thin?

Be yourself! A warm heart
Is what will set YOU apart
From all those hungry nervous wrecks
Of women a sensible man rejects.
They are too thin!

A lovely curve, a sparkling eye
Are better than letting life pass by
As you sweat away an extra pound,
Who cares if you are square or round
When, like the goddesses above,
YOU can offer the world your love?

Barbara Cartland

Chapter One

Introduction

Since earliest childhood I have always loved beauty and longed to be beautiful. I have wished to have those around me beautiful too.

When I was twenty-five it seemed to me the most terrible thing that in a few years my face would lose its youth and comeliness and I should grow to look like some of the middle-aged women I knew.

I used to sit opposite people in buses and trains, especially women of forty-five or more, and study their faces. It became a kind of obsession with me. There was I, twenty-five and good-looking, watching the various expressions of what I might become in twenty short years.

How I detested this look of middle-age!

My husband used to laugh at me and say that the thing that really mattered was what was inside a face – what it stood for, so to speak. If it expressed courage, kindliness and generosity, it didn't matter much that there were a few lines and wrinkles on it.

The higher side of my character agreed with him in principle. All the same, I felt that I would give anything not to develop those ugly lines and folds of skin, even if they might bespeak courage, kindliness and generosity.

From that time on I began to study faces from a new point of view. What did they express?

Well, for example, travelling in a train one day I looked round me, and what did I see? Opposite sat a woman of about fifty, whose face seemed to express that she ate far too much and never took any exercise.

Next to her was a woman of about forty-five, she was carrying a tennis racquet, so she evidently took lots of exercise. She was scraggy in the extreme. She had more wrinkles than the fat one and her face expressed discontent and strain. Who knows, poor thing, perhaps she had once been pretty!

Further on was a dear old lady, much older than either of the others – quite seventy-five, I should say. Her hair was white. And yet, though she was obviously an older woman, for some reason her face hadn't aged in an ugly way. There were no thick rhinoceros folds round her neck and chin. Nor were there any deep grooves and lines from the corner of her nose to her mouth. There were some lines round her eyes, it's true, but her whole face expressed sweetness and gaiety. Looking at her, I thought my husband's words were largely justified.

Nevertheless I wasn't happy. I wanted something for myself that was more than a beautiful old age, something that my studies led me to know was much rarer, and that was a beautiful *middle* age.

There isn't space here to consider all the types I used to watch and observe. Suffice it to say that I did so for some years and came at various times to various conclusions.

An experience that left a great impression on my mind a short time later was the following.

I was bathing on the sea-coast with M., a friend of mine, a woman of about fifty. We undressed behind some rocks, and for the first time I saw her naked body. I confess I was surprised to notice how young and beautiful her body was. Her face had all the signs of the fifty-year-old woman, but not her body. Here were no wrinkles or sagging flesh, but firm, beautiful, taut muscles like a girl's.

I pondered on the problem. Why should M. have the body of a young woman and the face of an old one?

Now M. had always been athletic. She swam, rode and did physical exercises before breakfast in the morning and generally led a very healthy life. So then and there an idea was born in my mind. M.'s body was beautiful because the muscles were firm and strong from exercise. Would it be possible therefore, I wondered, to invent a system of physical exercises for the facial muscles which would also keep them firm and strong, and prevent them from sagging and drooping in the usual hideous manner of old age? From that time on my mind played with the this idea, as I continued to observe all and sundry.

I am now middle-aged myself, and I really do believe that after ten years of study I have discovered and worked out a system of facial muscle exercise, whereby, if it is used systematically and persistently, a youthful appearance of the face may be prolonged far into middle life, and that old age when it does come may be beautiful, with none of its deforming and hideous aspects.

A woman doesn't reach maturity until she is twenty. At thirty the mid-Victorians thought that she should put on a cap and climb up on the shelf, an arrangement which gave her just ten years of youth out of a possible ninety. Even today people consider that the perfect beauty of a woman's face fades by forty. This allows the poor thing twenty years out of ninety! True, she may go on being an attractive woman after forty – more attractive mentally and spiritually sometimes than in early youth, because if she is the right sort she will have gained in sympathy and understanding – but the radiance of her physical beauty will be on the wane.

To return to my observations on middle-aged faces, I remarked that certain peculiarities were present in either a greater or a lesser degree in all of them: there was generally a marked fold or line running from the corner of the nose to the mouth. Also there were two little lines going from the corners of the mouth downwards. Usually two vertical creases marred the beauty of the forehead just between the eyebrows and horizontal lines ran across the forehead, while underneath the eyes were crowsfeet and bags and pouches in varying degrees.

So much for the most disfiguring age-lines of the face. The ugliest feature of all in decadence is the chin. On a plump woman as age approaches it will hang in double – even, oh horror, triple – folds! On a thin woman it becomes scrawny, like an old chicken's.

And yet this line from the tip of the chin to under the chin and down the throat is one of the loveliest lines a young woman's face possesses. It should curve so beautifully if the bony shape of the chin and throat are well formed.

Of course, one must realise at the outset that nobody can change the shape of the bones. If someone has a receding chin or a projecting nose, it can't be altered.* What I do claim, however, is that a person can remain as good-looking in middle-life as at twenty-five or thirty, provided these exercises are begun not later than thirty or thirty-five and are practised consistently.

Women of all ages may be improved and the degeneration in the muscle checked, but the best results will naturally be obtained by beginning early, as prevention is always easier than cure: once lines are deeply formed in the skin *they can be greatly lessened and the whole flesh of the face toned up* by my system of exercises, but if I can get a woman to begin doing them before she has any deep lines, I see no reason why she should ever develop any.

Nevertheless, if you are over forty-five, don't be down-hearted. I have persuaded a lady I know, who is sixty, to do a course of this treatment. She has been working at it now for about six months, and already her face looks marvellously better and much younger in every way.

But for the older woman I would say this. *Don't overdo the exercises and tire out your face muscles, or you will think that because you have a drawn look the treatment is doing you no good.* Go at the exercises very gently, but very steadily, for the first three

---

* These words were written before the modern developments of cosmetic surgery, but they remain true even now for most people. (B.C.)

months. Instead of doing the movements about five times, as I have advocated, begin by doing them each only once every day, and then gradually increase at the rate of one more each week, until you are doing the full number. You will realise when you have finished this chapter that if you are over forty-five your face muscles will have softened and lost a great deal of tone, so you can't expect them to bear at first the amount of exercise that a young woman's will. Later, when you have gradually redeveloped them, you can do each exercise five or even ten times every day, but not to begin with!

You may find you can't learn an exercise properly unless you practise it several times. This is probably true. Therefore learn only one at a time, and when you have mastered it do it once, or at most twice, and at the same time learn one more new one, and so on.

I said just now that I had been studying this matter of physical exercises of the face for ten years. This is true, but don't imagine that it will take you all this time to master the subject. You must remember that when I began I had nothing to go on but an idea.

It is one thing to learn up a few long Latin names of face muscles out of a textbook, as I began by doing, together with their places in the face and their uses in daily life. It is quite another to invent exercises that will counteract the bad effects of face muscles which have been brought into play wrongly, for purposes of frowning, showing surprise or perhaps ill-temper. Not to mention the re-education of muscles that were used by man when he was in a primitive state of evolution and are seldom or never worked with now.

Thinking out all this took time. The ideas came to me bit by bit, and as they came I practised them. Some seemed to do more good than others. Gradually I weeded out the useless ones. Keeping only to the best, I evolved a system which is really based on two very simple principles. They are briefly these:

1. Wherever there is a muscle that will draw the flesh of the face in one direction, there is another which opposes its action, which may be educated to draw it back again into the opposite direction.

2. Age tends, partly through wrong use of muscles and partly through general slackening of fibre, to make all the flesh of the face droop forwards and downwards towards the central points of the nose, mouth and chin.

Chapter Two

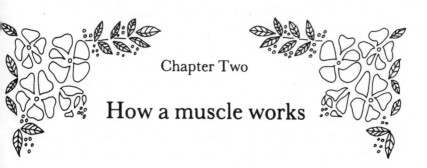

Chapter Two

How a muscle works

We must try to understand something of the way a muscle works.

I don't intend to be technical or to use scientific terms, because I'm not writing for medical students, so I will try to explain the principle by a simple though fanciful illustration.

Think of a muscle as a child's toy balloon before it is blown up. It is then a long, slack, empty bag of fine skin. Now place an imaginary hook at each end of the slack balloon. Then imagine that these hooks are attached at the tops and bottoms to other hooks, belonging to other slack balloons.

Imagine that all these little balloons are suddenly blow up. They will lose in length and become quite fat and round.

Now, feeding these muscle balloons are very fine blood-vessels called capillaries, and when the slack muscle balloons expand, as they do when they begin to work, the capillaries dilate also. So when you work any muscle, not only do you harden and enlarge its outer coat, but you draw to it a large supply of fresh blood.

This latter action, I consider, plays an important part in my exercises, for the increased blood supply which is brought about is one of the best things for the face.

Now, to return to our lesson. Imagine that all round the muscle balloons and the capillaries there are also the fat cells. Let's watch what happens. If you blow out the muscle cells by hard work, they get hungry and make a bigger call upon the blood, as already explained. The blood, to maintain this extra supply, in turn calls upon the fat cells, which are really little store-cupboards of reserve food. The fat cells are thus re-absorbed by the blood, while the muscle cells expand in proportion.

If, on the other hand, the muscle cells are never used, as is the case with any part that isn't properly exercised, the blood supply to them dwindles and the nourishment which should go to them is deposited instead as fat cells, which increase with alarming rapidity as the quality of the flesh degenerates.

It is as if all the food you should be eating were locked up in the pantry instead of being served up for dinner. You would be hungry, though there would really be plenty of food in the house.

That is the position of the muscle-cells when they aren't stimulated by use. They become starved and degenerate, while the nourishment which they require so badly is being locked up in the useless fat cells.

Of course, fat has its proper uses in the body. A certain amount is essential to health, for together with the blood it feeds the nerves and also in the right proportions gives a gentle roundness and beauty of outline to the face and form. The ideal to be aimed at from an aesthetic point of view is to get the correct proportions of fat and muscle into the flesh.

Athletes who devote their lives to physical activity develop very large muscles, too large for what would be considered beautiful in a woman. Well, I'm not proposing that you should develop your face muscles to this extent. If you did, you would end up with a bull-like neck and heavy cheeks. But if you have two chins, these, believe me, aren't caused by muscular development, but by an invasion of fat cells in your flesh.

On the other hand, if you are very thin, don't be afraid that exercising the muscles will make you look thinner. Far from it, because as you build up your muscles they will begin to take the place of your missing fat and your hollows will fill out. Who has ever heard of a scraggy athlete? Athletes are always well-covered and healthy-looking.

The action of a muscle in drawing blood to itself is, I consider, very important to the effect of my exercises for keeping youth and beauty in the face. The reason is fairly obvious, I think. The blood is the life. In it are contained all the gland secretions and nourishment of the body that are necessary for its upkeep and well-being.

Therefore if you draw blood to the flesh of any given part you nourish and renew it.

Now that I have explained in a somewhat fanciful way how muscles work, I will try to teach you some of the exercises which, if persisted with, will keep you looking young and attractive for many years to come.

Chapter Three

Chapter Three

The four areas
of the head, face and neck

You must remember that the skin of your face is extremely delicate. If you have a little cat, watch the way she treats herself, how softly and lovingly she washes herself with her soft paws. Well, think of your fingers as paws and remember how the cat lubricates her paws before she grooms herself. Of course you won't want to lick your fingers!! But you must cream your face well with a wholesome natural unguent before attempting any of the following exercises. Then, in considering them, think of the neck, face and head as being divided into four areas (see p. 19), as follows:

1. The whole of the neck, from the collar-bones upward to the tip of the chin, and also at the back up to the line where the hair grows.

2. The part of the face from the tip of the chin along the jaw-bones to a point behind the ears, and a line taken back again down the cheeks to the corner of the mouth.

3. A line along the forehead above the eyebrows to a point behind the ears. This line then comes down behind and under the ears and meets the one which forms the top part of the Second Area.

4. This Area comprises all the top of the head down to where the lines of the Third Area starts, and down the back of the head to where the First Area begins.

You will notice that these imaginary lines of the First, Second and Third Areas come together at a point behind the ears. This is very important. I will explain the reason later on.

Now for each of the four areas of the neck, face and head, I have a set of exercises which I have designed to control, develop and strengthen the muscles of the particular parts described.

You must trust to my ten years of study and practice, and believe me when I tell you that those concerned with the First, Second and Third Areas are by far the easiest. Therefore learn and practise them first.

Most of you probably won't be able to do the Auricular Series of exercises (Chapter Eight) or the movements connected with the Fourth Area until you have practised for some weeks. I couldn't do them myself for a long time. So please trust me, and don't try to run before you can walk. The exercises for the First and Second and Third Areas deal mostly with the muscles of the face which are in daily use, whereas the exercises for the Auricular Series are used largely in connection with the fine sheath-like layer of tiny surface muscles, which are very much more difficult to control.

To give you an example of what I mean: if an impatient person tries to perform the second part of Exercise E in the Auricular Series, which is to be used for the correction of lines under the eyes, before she has made herself absolute mistress of Exercise A in the Auricular Series, which entirely controls the movement, she will probably do herself far more harm than good. All she will succeed in doing is to wrinkle up her eyes as though a strong light were shining in them and thereby produce many more lines round them than she had before.

So, with this word of caution, let's learn how to do the exercises of the First Area.

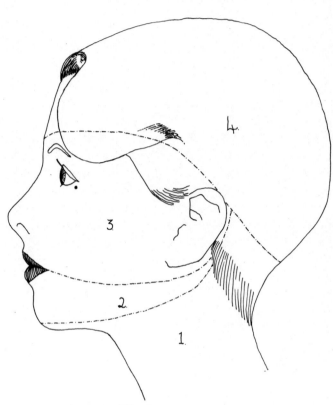

The four areas.

Chapter Four

 Chapter Four

Six exercises for the First Area

No. 1. Exercise for the chin muscles

Take a hardcover book of average size. Hold it in both hands, so that the two ends rest on the lower part of the palms, not on the fingers. Now place the flat, broad side of the cover right under the chin, so that the chin sits on the book, so to speak, and the edge of it touches the neck where the throat and chin join:

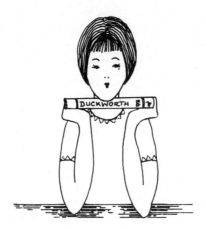

Exercise for the chin muscles.

Then press the book up very hard against the chin, and as you do so open your mouth as if you were *forcing it open* against the pressure of the book, *which is forcing it shut*.

This exercise will set and harden the chin muscles, and if persisted in *for sufficient time regularly* will remove any double chin or slackening throat muscles. If, on the other hand, the chin and neck are too thin, it will develop the muscles and make them appear rounded and fuller.

Practise the exercise as follows:

Press the book up and force the mouth open and hold them in this position while you count to yourself 1 to 10.

Relax pressure and then repeat the movement, counting 10 to 20.

Relax pressure and repeat the movement, counting 20 to 30.

Relax pressure and repeat the movement, counting 40 to 50.

Do this for two months and then if desired add another 50 as before, with a relaxation after each 10.

Increase the number of exercises to as many as you wish, but always on the principle of 50 added every two months.

Caution. If you overdo the movement at first, you will work off too much fat, strain your muscles and *look worse than you did before*. This development, like any other muscular training, must be done gently at first. Begin by doing the exercise *a few times*, and work up to a larger amount *by slow degrees as the muscles concerned get stronger*.

No. 2. Second exercise for the chin muscles

Proceed as for No. 1, but instead of putting the flat part of the book under the centre of the chin, place it on the right and tuck it well in under the side of the jaw.

Then practise the exercise in the same way as No. 1. That is to say, push the book up under the side of the chin and force the mouth open against the pressure of the book, which is forcing it shut.

Hold it in this position and count 1 to 10. Then relax the muscles and repeat the exercise, counting 10 to 20.

Do this movement five times, which will bring your counting up to 50, as in No. 1.

Next, put the back of the book under the *left* side of the chin and repeat the whole exercise as before.

After you have worked at it for two months, increase the number of movements to ten times.

The power of resistance in muscular exercises

Before going further, I must refer to what I call using the power of resistance as an aid to muscular development.

For example, if you try to lift a heavy bag with your hand, the weight of the bag resists your effort to lift it, and this calls forth from the muscles of your arm a still greater effort, so that they swell out and become hard. If you had merely picked up a piece of paper from the floor, there would have been no weight resistance and the muscles in your arm wouldn't have enlarged appreciably.

It is this power of resistance that you use when you do the exercise that I have described with the book under the chin. If you simply open your mouth, that doesn't set the muscle; but when you use the resisting power of the book trying to force your mouth shut against the effort of your mouth to remain open, you get a good illustration of what I mean.

Anybody who knows anything about physical exercises as used in drills and gymnasiums will understand me when I talk about 'setting a muscle'. For those who don't I must try to explain my meaning.

It is possible to resist one muscle with another and to set it and make it hard by working its corresponding muscle against it. As an illustration, visualise a long pole hinged at one end, with two men, one at each side, trying to pull it over with a rope.

Next, imagine the pole hinged as before, but with a bit sticking out beyond the hinge, one man pulling with a rope above the hinge and the other pulling with a rope below the hinge.

The strongest man will pull the pole over.

This is exactly what happens in the arm muscles. Your forearm is the pole, and along the top of your upper arm bone is the *biceps* muscle, which is trying to pull your arm towards your shoulder. Underneath your upper arm bone is the *triceps* muscle, which is pulling from below the hinge and trying to force your forearm away from your shoulder.

The reason I mention the arm muscles is that you can so easily find them for yourself. Consequently they illustrate, in a way that you can't mistake, the principle of resistance.

Now make this experiment:

Kneel at a table so that your right armpit is on a level with its top, your right upper arm-bone is lying horizontally on the table and your right forearm is poised upright. Then ask a friend to hold the hand of the raised forearm in such a way that your hand can either push or pull against it. Now place your left hand on the right upper-arm, which is on the table.

You will find that when you try to *pull your right hand towards your shoulder* you will feel the *biceps muscle* hardening in the right upper-arm, while if you *push your right hand away from you*, you will feel the *triceps muscle* hardening.

The reason why these muscles set is that they are trying to overcome the pressure of your friend's hand. With a little practice you will find that you can set both muscles working against each other without the aid of any artificial pressure.

Exactly on the same principle, in the sides of your face and neck there are muscles which *open* your mouth and in your cheeks and temples there are muscles which *close* it.

Now attempt the following:

Try to open and shut the mouth at the same time. This sounds nonsense, but is really possible; and when you can do it you will be able to set the muscles in the cheeks, chin and throat without the aid of any book or artificial pressure.

When practising this exercise, place the fingers of each hand lightly in the middle of each cheek, so that you can feel when the muscles begin to work and get hard.

Don't shut the teeth for this exercise. On the contrary, keep the mouth wide open, and then a little less open until you get the sensation of the muscles in your cheeks coming into play under your fingers. When you have learnt to do this you can proceed to Exercises Nos. 3 and 4 in the First Area.

I shall often speak about this power of resistance in the following pages, so I hope that you will make a study of the subject. It is possible to set the muscles in this way in any part of the body, legs or arms, and also of course, in the head, face and neck.

Continue doing the first and second exercises of the First Area *with the book*, even after you have learnt to set the muscles without its aid, because it makes such a good straight line under the chin and prevents any possibility of a double chin.

Now, having digressed on this important matter of 'muscular resistance', we will proceed to learn some more exercises for the First Area.

No. 3. Exercise for the principal muscles of the chin, throat and neck

The following can be practised in the morning before rising.

Lie flat on the back without a pillow.

Slowly raise the head about six inches and hold it in this position. As you do so, open the mouth and set the cheek and chin muscles as described.

Then let the head sink slowly back, keeping the muscles in the cheeks and chin set all the time. Count as follows:

> Raise head, count 1 to 10.
> Lower head, count 10 to 20.
> Relax all muscles and rest.

Repeat this whole movement four times, which will bring

your counting up to 80.

After you have worked at it for two months increase the number of movements to eight times.

No. 4. Second exercise for the principal muscles of the chin,
throat and neck

Proceed exactly as for No. 3.

When the head has been raised and the muscles set in the cheeks and chin, turn the head as far as possible to the right, and then as far as possible to the left.

Do this slowly ten times. Then let the head sink back and rest a moment.

Practise this whole movement three times.

After you have worked at it for two months, increase the number of movements to eight times.

No. 5. Exercise for the neck muscles

Have you ever noticed how middle-aged women, if they are at all fat, tend to get a roll of flesh running across the back of the neck? If you are one of these, the following exercise will help you counteract this unfortunate development.

Place the tips of the fingers on each shoulder. Then raise the shoulders up as high as they will go.

Next, bend the shoulder bones backwards, as if you were trying to press your shoulder blades together. As you do so, the head should go back too, until the lower part of the back of the head touches the upper part of the shoulder blades.

Practise this exercise as follows:

Get into the position described above and count 1 to 10.
Relax all the muscles.
Repeat the exercise, counting 10 to 20.

Do this movement five times, which will bring your counting up to 50.

After you have worked at it for two months, increase the number of movements to ten times.

No. 6. Exercise for filling out a thin throat

Take a handkerchief and gently blow your nose, not because it requires blowing, but as an exercise for the throat.

Clasp your throat with the other hand while you do so and you will feel how the muscular effort fills out all hollows. A gentle coughing does the same thing, but is apt to irritate the larynx.

Continue to blow the nose gently about twenty times, keeping the throat clasped with the other hand in the process.

This exercise is excellent for a neck that is beginning to fade and become shrivelled, but be careful not to blow the nose too violently.

Chapter Five

Chapter Five

Five exercises for the Second Area

It is the slackening and softening of the muscles in the Second Area of the face (see p. 19) that produces the appearance of uneven cheek and chin line and drooping at the corners of the mouth which is so unsightly in middle age.

The following exercises are designed to counteract these faults.

No. 1. Exercise for the jaw muscles

Sit at a table and place the elbows on it, in such a way that the hands support the face.

Place the base of the palms just where they join the wrists, so that they press hard against the lower jaw – that is to say, just above where the lower dotted line comes marking the Second Area.

This done, clench the teeth tightly, so that (as was described in Exercise No. 1 of the First Area) there is a pressure outwards and a pressure inwards, making a resistance.

This will set the large jaw-bone muscles, as you will soon feel, since they are the most powerful muscles in the face.

Proceed to do the exercise as follows:

Press the cheeks, clench the teeth and count from 1 to 10.
Relax pressure of hands and teeth.
Press the cheeks, clench the teeth and count from 10 to 20.

Relax pressure of hands and teeth.

Perform the movement five times, which will bring your counting up to 50.

After two months' practice, do the exercise ten times.

No. 2. Exercise for the buccinator muscle

This is an amusing exercise, and will make you look slightly comic! But don't despise it on that account, because it is one of the best there is for cheeks that are getting flabby and losing their tone.

Buccinator means the 'trumpet-blowing' muscle of the cheek.

So now, try to blow an imaginary trumpet. Purse your lips tightly, and at the same time fill your cheeks with wind. But instead of blowing out through your mouth, hold the lips shut.

Now place the three middle fingers of each hand on each cheek at either side of the mouth, just where the *buccinator* muscles are, and press your fingers in against the blown-out surface of the cheeks. This will make you feel that the air *must* come out through your lips. *But don't let it.* Hold it in, and the resistance of the fingers pressing against the wind in the cheek will cause the *buccinator* muscles to set and get quite hard, as they do if you blow a trumpet.

Practise the exercise as follows:

Blow out the cheeks and press in the fingers. Count 1 to 10.
Relax pressure of cheeks and hands.
Blow out the cheeks and press in the fingers. Count 10 to 20.
Relax pressure of cheeks and hands.
Repeat this movement five times, which will bring your counting up to 50.

After two months' practice, perform the exercise ten times.

No. 3. Exercise for the muscles at the point of the chin

In middle age, women who have rather large jaws, and some others too, are apt to get a drooping of the point of the chin. This is partly what causes the look of double chin.

It isn't enough to work away the flesh under the throat as we did in a previous exercise. The *tip* of the chin must be drawn up also, as the muscle has become slack and the flesh has drooped.

Whenever we speak, this muscle is in action, and after forty years or so of hard work it gets tired of going down and begins to stay there!

So now we must find an exercise that will strengthen the lower lip and point of the chin and draw it up again to its original youthful outline. Here it is.

Clench the teeth fairly tightly – not uncomfortably, but just enough to harden the muscles a little.

Then place the three middle fingers of the right hand on the chin in such a manner that the tips of the fingers come about half an inch under the lower lip.

Now gently draw the flesh of the chin slightly downwards, as though you were wishing to increase its fall.

As you do so, push your lower lip up against your upper lip as if you were trying to make them both touch your nose. This should be done with the muscle in your lower lip and chin. All the time the fingers must be trying to draw it down again, as that makes the slight resistance which I have spoken about before and which always causes a muscle to work harder than if it had nothing to resist.

The exercise should be done as follows:

Draw up the flesh of the chin against the resistance of the fingers. Hold it in this position. Count 1 to 10.

Relax the muscles and pressure of the fingers.

Repeat the exercise. Count 10 to 20.

Relax the muscles and pressure of the fingers.

Do this movement five times, which will bring your counting up to 50.

After two months' practice, you may do the exercise ten times.

No. 4. Exercise for the muscles at the sides of the chin

This exercise is to be used on the same principle as No. 3, but is meant not for the point of the chin, but for the flesh on either side of it.

The most important muscles in the Second Area come up from under the sides of the chin towards the corners of the mouth, and when they lose their elasticity, as they do in middle-life, they begin to sag and you get those ugly lines running down from the sides of the lower lip which suggest peevishness and ill-temper.

In order to tighten and draw up these two little muscles again, practise the following exercise:

Proceed in the same way as for No. 3 of the Second Area. But use the middle fingers of each hand placed on either side of the chin, in such a way that the fingers lie along the muscles, the tips touching the corners of the mouth.

Now, exactly as for No. 3, draw the flesh very lightly a tiny bit downwards with the fingers, as though seeking to increase the fault.

As you do so, try to raise the flesh upwards by muscular effort working against the pressure of the fingers, thus making a resistance. Don't get this feeling by smiling, as that will produce a wrong result, but do your best actually to contract the muscles upwards.

When you have learnt to do this movement and have developed the muscles, you will feel them under your fingers working like hard cords.

The exercise should be practised as follows:

Draw up the flesh as advised against the pressure of the fingers, and hold it in this position. Count 1 to 10.

Relax the muscles and pressure of the fingers.

Repeat the exercise. Count 10 to 20.

Relax the muscles and pressure of the fingers.

Do this movement five times, which will bring your counting up to 50.

After two months, practise the exercise ten times.

No. 5. Exercise for drawing up the surface muscles of the chin and jaw-bone areas

Place your two hands, one on either side of the face, so that the three middle fingers come just below the lobes of the ears, the tips of the fingers almost touching the bottom part of the lobes.

Now draw the fingers upwards in such a way that the flesh of the jaw is drawn up with them to a point slightly behind the ears.

As you do so, *clench the teeth together tightly*, so that the muscles set.

The exercise should be practised as follows:

Flesh drawn up by fingers, teeth clenched, count 1 to 10.

Relax the teeth and pressure of the fingers.

Repeat the exercise. Count 10 to 20.

Relax the teeth and pressure of the fingers.

Do this movement five times, which will bring your counting up to 50.

After two months, practise the exercise ten times.

When you have worked at it for a little while, experiment and see if you can do it without the help of the hands. That is to say, clench the teeth as before and *try to feel the surface muscles drawing up the flesh just as the fingers did*.

If you can't get this sensation at first, go on practising, as before, with the help of the hands, but in time you should be able to work the muscles in the surface of the flesh upwards towards the ears by clenching the teeth alone, and this will tighten the skin up all along the jaw-bone.

Chapter Six

 Chapter Six

Five exercises for the Third Area

No. 1. Exercise for the cheek muscles

The main cheek muscles to be concerned with ascend on each side like two little straps. They lift the top lip when you smile and draw it upwards slightly towards the eyes.

When, therefore, these muscles become slack, you see them sagging and circular lines forming under the eyes. Where they get slack at their lower ends you find lines coming from the corners of the nose to the corners of the mouth.

Here is the exercise that will counteract this loss of tone.

Place the first and second fingers of each hand on either side of the nose, with the tips pointing upwards. Very slightly spread them out in such a way that they reach to the edge of the bones of the eye sockets. These can be felt very distinctly under the skin just below the edge of the under eyelids. The idea is that the fingers should lie along the two little strap-shaped muscles in question.

In time, when these become developed, you will be able to feel them under the skin; but for the present you must try to discover their presence as nearly as possible.

Having got your position correctly, close the mouth and push your lower lip up against your upper lip, as if you were trying to make them both go up towards your eyes.

If you do this movement correctly, you will find that the flesh under your fingers is pushed up by the lips.

Note. Don't purse up the mouth, as if kissing, in this exercise. If you do, it will *only push up the nose*! On the contrary, *keep the lips in a slightly smiling position,* and then press them upwards. This will move the flesh on either side of the nose towards the eyes.

At first, if the muscles feel weak, you can help them to draw up by *pushing* the fingers a little towards the eyes, as you press the lips upwards. But when the muscles develop and get stronger, you should begin to use a small amount of resistance. That is to say, instead of pushing the fingers upwards, press them very slightly downwards, at the same time drawing the lips up. This will cause the muscles in question to set.

Practise the exercise as follows:

Push the muscles upwards and hold the position while you count 1 to 10.

Relax the muscles and pressure of the fingers.

Repeat the movement. Count 10 to 20.

Relax the muscles and pressure of the fingers.

Do this exercise five times, which will bring your counting up to 50.

After two months' practice, you may increase the number to ten times.

No. 2. Second exercise for the cheek muscles

In the Third Area you must also consider two more long, strap-like muscles which run from the corners of the mouth upwards over the cheeks. It is when these get slack in conjunction with the other muscles in their neighbourhood that you get a look of drooping cheeks and also deep lines forming from the corners of the nose to the corners of the mouth. The following exercise will help to overcome this fault.

Place the first and second fingers of each hand on either side of the face.

Clench the teeth and smile. As you do so, press the flesh

under the second fingers slightly upwards and the flesh under the first fingers outwards.

Practise this exercise as follows:

Push the muscles upwards and outwards and smile.

Hold this position with clenched teeth while you count 1 to 10.

Relax the muscles and pressure of the fingers.

Repeat the exercise, counting 10 to 20. Relax the muscles and pressure of the fingers.

Do this movement five times, which will bring your counting up to 50.

After two months' practice, you may increase the number to ten times.

I do not recommend using much resistance in this one, as it tends to increase the lines between the nose and mouth.

No. 3. Exercise for the muscles round the eyes

When the muscles which go right round the eyes and enable you to close them get slack and lose their tone at their bottom edges, you find the flesh sagging and bagging under the eyes.

The following is an exercise that will help to counteract this fault. (But don't forget to cream your face first!)

Place the middle fingers of each hand at the outer corner of each eye.

Then draw back the flesh they are covering in a line towards the ears. If performed correctly, this action should draw back the corners of the eyes too, so that they become long, narrow 'ancient Egyptian eyes'.

Hold the flesh in this position. As you do so, close both eyes, gently at first and then gradually tighter and tighter, until at last you are squeezing the lids together against the pressure of the fingers holding them sideways. This will cause all the muscles round the eyes to work very hard indeed.

Keep them in this position while you count from 1 to 10.

Relax the muscles.

Repeat the exercise, counting 10 to 20.

Relax the muscles.

Do this movement five times, which will bring your counting up to 50.

After two months' practice, you may increase the number to ten times.

Be sure *not to close one eye at a time* white doing this, so that you may watch yourself in the looking-glass, because that will cause you to wrinkle up your nose and mouth sideways, and this makes lines round them.

The correct way is to *close both eyes at once, and to try to keep the nose and mouth perfectly quiet*. Also, do your best not to frown as you press the lids together.

When you have learnt the auricular (ear) movements, (Chapter Eight), you should always follow this exercise with the second part of Exercise E of the Auricular Series. This will draw out any surface lines you may have made by practising the exercise and working the deeper muscles under the skin.

These two exercises, one following the other, should in time remove any harsh lines or saggy bags under the eyes.

However, until you have mastered the Auricular Series, you may practise this exercise alone, as it will greatly strengthen the deeper muscles and will draw up any drooping flesh round the eyes.

No. 4. Exercise for the muscles round the mouth

Another circular muscle which you must be concerned with goes all round the mouth.

The bottom part of it really belongs to the Second Area, but as the top half belongs to the Third Area, I am putting it in here.

It is an extremely important muscle in the face because nearly all the others have some form of attachment to it. Therefore, when you exercise it thoroughly and keep it young and firm, to a minor degree you develop most of the others at the same time.

If you watch and observe, as I have done for many years, you will notice that the lips of women do one of two things as they grow old. Either they become thin and pinched, or they become rather bloated and fat; and this, curiously enough, doesn't always bear any relation to whether the whole body gains or loses in weight. Sometimes a very thin woman will develop large coarse lips, while a fat one will get a narrow, mean-looking mouth.

The lovely lines of the *youth mouth* seldom survive the fortieth year. Indeed it is this ageing lip-formation that does more than anything else (in my opinion) to take the look of youth from a woman's face. She may preserve her skin with great care and success, but except in rare instances the lines of her mouth will nearly always give her away.

The following exercise will do much to preserve the beauty of the lips.

If the lips are becoming a thin, uninteresting line, it will develop the muscles and they will get fuller. On the other hand, if they are coarsening and thickening, it will reduce the fat and bring back their original curves.

Here it is. You will see that it is an easy one to learn and practise.

Keep the lips in their *normal* position – that is to say, *don't* pinch them up as if kissing.

Press the bottom lip up as hard as ever you can against the top lip. At the same time press the top lip down as hard as you can against the bottom lip, thus making a resistance between the two.

Hold them in this position while you count 1 to 10.

Relax the muscles.

Repeat the exercise. Count 10 to 20.

Relax the muscles.

Do this movement five times, which will bring your counting up to 50.

After two months, you may increase the number to ten times.

When you have finished the exercise, you should, if you have done it properly, feel a warm glow in the lips as the blood begins to circulate there.

No. 5. An exercise that will teach you to smile in such a way that few, if any, lines are formed round the mouth

Have you ever considered the reason why certain people make such deep-furrowed lines between the nose and mouth when laughing?

It is because they smile only with their mouths. The whole of the rest of the flesh of their faces keeps practically still.

The lips expand and move back to meet a stiff wall of cheek on either side and so those hard, unattractive wrinkles are formed.

I know a young girl of nineteen who has these lines marked already more deeply than I have, and I long to tell her how to avoid them. But young women are sometimes so certain that they know best about everything that so far I have refrained from doing so.

Now there are other people who smile with their whole faces. Not only do their lips expand, which action by itself produces a meaningless grin, but their eyes and cheeks seems to smile too and their whole expression looks joyous and merry.

The real reason for this is that the flesh of the cheeks, instead of remaining fixed, goes up towards the eyes, and also a little back towards the ears.

In truth, as I said before, it isn't only their lips that smile, but their whole faces.

These people don't get those hard wrinkles round their mouths, even when they are getting on in years, because they laugh in such a way that the lines never get deeply formed.

Place the hands on either side of the cheeks in such a way that the tips of the fingers come just below the eyes, and the other ends of the fingers, where they join on to the palms of the hands, come just below the corners of the mouth.

Then smile. As you do so, press the flesh of the cheeks upwards and outwards towards the eyes and ears.

Practise this exercise in front of a looking-glass as follows:

Smile and draw up cheeks with the hands. Count 1 to 10.
Relax the smile and remove the pressure of your hands.
Repeat the exercise, counting 10 to 20.
Relax the smile and the pressure of your hands.
Do this whole movement five times.

When you have been working at it for some time and can feel that you are getting control over the muscles, try to make the same facial movements without the help of the hands.

As soon as you can do this quite easily *as an exercise*, try gradually to get into the habit of smiling in this way, with the whole face.

I don't want you to become self-conscious in your smile. *Far from it.* But if, as I say, you gradually form a habit, it will very soon become second nature, and you won't have to think about it any more.

Chapter Seven

Chapter Seven

The Auricular Series
and how I discovered it

The Auricular Series of exercises, which control the fine surface muscles of the skin of the face in the Second and Third Areas, are the most difficult that you will have to learn.

Look at page 19 and you will see that these areas consist of a kind of triangle on each side of the face, with its points coming just behind the ears.

You will remember that in Chapter One I drew your attention to the fact that age tends to make all the muscles of the face fall forwards and downwards towards the nose, mouth and chin, so that the flesh sags into lines under the eyes, especially from the corners of the nose to the corners of the mouth.

Bearing this in mind, make the following experiment.

Sit in front of a looking-glass in such a manner that the light comes from the right or left, but not from in front.

Place the first, second and third fingers of each hand on either side of the face, so that the first two fingers come just in front of the ears and the third finger one inch below the outer corners of the eyes, the second being placed midway between the other two.

This done, slightly raise the flesh of the face by pressing up the fingers.

Do you see that by doing this you have drawn out all lines round the nose, mouth and chin and look much younger?

Of course, if you are twenty you won't notice any great difference, but if you are thirty or forty-five, you will wish, I feel certain, that you could obtain this result permanently.

Well, I have discovered some exercises which, if persisted in regularly, will so lift and strengthen the muscles that are near the surface of the skin that you will largely get the desired result. But, as I said before, these movements are difficult to learn and require some patience.

Three small fan-like muscles spread up the head just behind and above the ears.

These muscles are very important little fellows for our purpose, as it is through them that control may be gained over the sheath-like layer of fine muscular tissue which extends all over the surface of the forehead, cheeks and chin.

Long ago, when man was still primitive – when, perhaps, he was not very far removed from a monkey man – it was with the aid of these little auricular muscles that he used to prick up his ears, just as an animal does, when he heard sounds that led him to suppose that an enemy was approaching!

Most modern men and women have lost this power to raise their ears, but every now and then you come across someone who, though not uncivilised in any other way, has retained as a strange heritage from the past this knowledge of how to move the ears up and down.

Thirty years ago, when I was a little girl at school, I had a great friend, Isabel. She possessed this curious power and, believe me, it was looked upon as a great accomplishment among us little girls! Whenever we were supposed to be particularly good and quiet during prep, Isabel, having previously gained the attention of the whole class, would proceed to prick her ears, with awful results, as we would all giggle violently!

Isabel used to sit beside me during these mirth-provoking exhibitions, and I would study her profile. She became so proficient in ear-raising, from having performed her weird trick so often for our benefit, that I used to observe that when she made the muscular efforts necessary to prick her ears, *part of the sides of her cheeks would be pulled up with them.*

At the time this merely amused me, and I didn't attach any importance to it. *But now listen.* Many years afterwards when, having studied face muscles, I was on the look-out for an exercise that would lift the cheeks and pull up the surface muscles of the skin in their neighbourhood, *I suddenly remembered Isabel and her quaint habit.*

Combing back my hair, I gazed at those impotent little members of mine and wondered if I could ever learn to raise them as Isabel had done.

I tried and tried. And then I tried again. But no, they seemed quite stuck.

However, I persevered for about a month at odd times, when I was reading, or walking. To my great delight, one day I found that I could just move them very slightly.

Encouraged by this auricular activity, I continued to try and try again, and at last with perseverance I gained complete mastery over my ears and could twitch them up and down.

To raise the ears alone, however, was but the beginning of my ambition, for Isabel had been able to move the whole skin of her cheeks back together with her ears. So I practised patiently until by degrees I got control of all the surface muscles of the cheek, *continuing to use the ear as the principal centre of lifting* – THE LEVER, SO TO SPEAK.

I found, as I gained more and more power, that not only could I do this, *but I was also able to control the surface muscles in the skin of the forehead*, so that when I drew my ears up and back I could pull the surface of the forehead muscle sideways, and by doing so could draw out the little vertical lines that came between my eyebrows.

Now look at the six diagrams overleaf. Imagine for a moment that *yours* is the face depicted thereon:

First A. Here you have raised the ears alone, upwards, outwards and backwards.

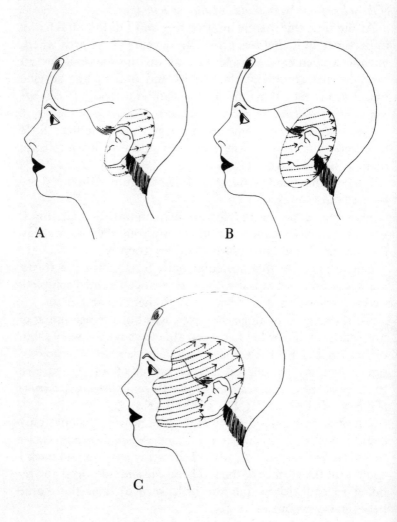

The Auricular Series of Exercises, including the *Great Triangular Pull* (F).

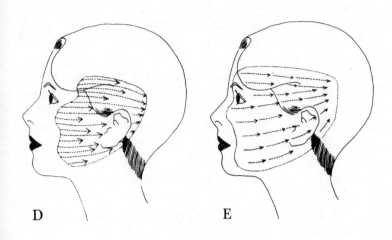

D   E

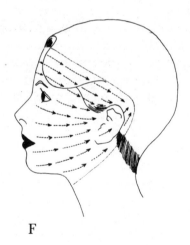

F

In B, you have lifted the ears and also the flesh round the front and bottoms of them for the space of about one inch.

In C, still further control has been gained, so that the flesh can be raised to a point half-way down the cheeks, and the surface muscles on the temples can be felt moving slightly backwards towards the ears.

By this time you have not only got control over the ear muscles but have begun to feel a slight power of movement in that sheath-like layer of fine muscular tissues which covers the forehead and the cheeks and which seems to be intimately connected with the auricular muscles.

By D, you can feel most of the cheek moving up with the ears. The surface muscles on the forehead are also beginning to draw the flesh over the eyebrows backwards towards the ears, in such a way that the two little vertical lines between the eyebrows (which inhabit most faces of over thirty) are being slowly but surely pressed out, by the muscle under the skin getting pulled back.

When you come to E, you will have developed still further control. You will be able to feel the fine skin muscles below the eyes moving sideways and the surface muscles round the chin and throat, too, all drawing upwards and outwards, until at last you will get what I have christened the *Great Triangular Pull*.

You will see that we have now largely accomplished what we set out to do.

But to do it patience and perseverance must be your watchwords.

I know it's possible, because every day of my life I practise this *Great Triangular Pull*. But it took me more than a year to get full control of these surface muscles of the cheeks and forehead. I didn't spend long hours practising the movements in front of my glass. I'm much too busy for that. But while I was reading, walking, or driving I would try a little at a time, until at last I succeeded.

Well, the first thing you must do if you wish to proceed with this Auricular Series is to learn the exercise that controls all the others. Yes, you must journey backwards through time towards your prehistoric ancestors – *you must learn to prick your ears!*

In the next chapter, I will give separate exercises to help you gain the control I have advocated here.

Chapter Eight

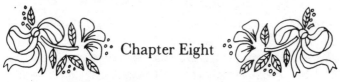

The Auricular Series described in detail

It is no use trying to learn all the exercises of this series at the same time.

The correct way to get the best results is as follows:

First learn to do A thoroughly. Take a month over it, or longer if necessary.

Then learn B in the same way and practise A and B together as one exercise.

After that learn C and practise A, B, C together as one exercise.

Following that, learn D, practising A, B, C, D together as one exercise.

Still later learn E, and practise A, B, C, D, E together as one exercise.

Last of all, learn F, and practise A, B, C, D, E, F together as one final and complete exercise, making the *Great Triangular Pull* (pages 54-5).

Exercise A of the Auricular Series

In my last chapter I told you that you had to control the muscles that raise your ears up and down before you could learn any of the subsidiary auricular exercises that are so important for the fine surface muscles of the Second and Third Areas of the face.

But I confess that to tell you to do so is easier than to tell you *how* to do so, unless of course, you happen to be a natural ear-mover!

Once you get the feeling that the ears are going up the tiniest bit, even though you can't see them doing so in your looking-glass, you will be well on the way to accomplishment.

Practise this sensation of movement and gradually it will get stronger and stronger, until at last you can have no doubt about it, as you will be able to see the ears going up and down quite plainly.

Now here are two ways to achieve this feeling:

1. Sit comfortably in an armchair with the back of your head resting on a cushion, in such a way that the ears are quite free.

Then begin to think about them. Think of them hard to the exclusion of everything else – EARS, EARS, EARS. Try to imagine that all your concentration and all your will-power are passing into your ears.

When you have been doing this for five minutes, suddenly clench the teeth tightly together. At the same time as the muscles set in the jaws, make a great effort to draw the ears back and up.

I said before, and I cannot repeat it too often, '*If at first you don't succeed, try, try, try again*'.

2. As an alternative method, make the effort this way.

Sit at your dressing-table opposite the looking-glass and put your elbows on the table.

Place the three middle fingers of each hand over each ear, and clench the teeth together. As you do so, push up your ears with your fingers.

Remain in this position while you count twenty slowly.

Relax and rest a moment and then *repeat the exercise over and over again*, until you begin to feel the muscles in your ears and jaws quite tired and achey.

When you have done this, try and see if you can move them

at all *by simply clenching the teeth and making a muscular effort without the help of the hands.*

Well, we will suppose that you have a slight sensation of power of movement at last. It has taken you a month or possibly longer to get this far.

Now don't be discouraged. Go on. Little by little you will get more and more control, until at last, one day, quite suddenly perhaps, you will feel that you really can raise your ears right up and down, so that you are able to see them doing so in the looking-glass, without any doubt about it.

Once having accomplished this exercise in your armchair, or at your dressing table, whichever you prefer, practise it at any odd moments while you are reading, driving or travelling.

When you really feel without any doubt that you can move your ears, you can greatly increase the power by using a little resistance, as I have so often advised before.

At this point, instead of *helping* them up with the fingers as when you were learning the exercises, use the fingers to press them gently *downwards* and draw them up with the ear muscles against the pressure.

It is no good whatever doing this in the early stages of the exercise, as your auricular muscles would be too undeveloped. I leave it to you to feel and know when you are sufficiently advanced to practise a slight resistance.

Exercise B of the Auricular Series

Having now gained control of the actual ears, try to feel the drawing up and back movement in the skin all round the fronts and bottoms of the ears, for the space of about one inch, on to the cheeks, as shown in Diagram B on p. 54.

To do this, sit in front of your looking-glass as before, with your elbows on the dressing-table. Place the three middle fingers of each hand on the cheeks, so that they come about one inch in front of the ears.

Having got this position correctly, clench the teeth, raise the ears, and as you do so push the flesh you are touching with your fingers so that *it goes upwards and backwards as well as the ears*.

Hold this position while you count 20 slowly. Then relax the teeth and ears and the pressure of the hands. *Don't remove the hands*, simply relax the pressure.

Repeat the movement as before.

Do this about twenty times.

Then remove your hands and try to do exactly the same thing without their help. That is to say, try to draw the flesh all round the fronts and bottoms of the ears up and back *with the ears* as you clench the teeth.

You will have to work at this for some time, as you did for Exercise A. But as soon as you can do it, without the help of the hands, practise it at odd times, as I suggested before.

When you can feel the movement quite strongly, begin to use a little resistance, as advocated in Exercise A of this series.

Exercise C of the Auricular Series

This exercise is to be done exactly on the same principle as the last one. But place the fingers of each hand lower on the cheeks.

The two third fingers should touch the cheekbones about one inch down from the outer corners of the eyes. The two first fingers should touch the jaw-bone about two inches down from the lobes of the ears. The middle fingers should come at an equal length between the other two.

Having spaced these correctly, proceed to clench the teeth, draw the ears backwards and upwards, and at the same time push up the flesh of the face with the fingers.

As I have described in Exercise B, practise this until you

can at last do it without the help of your hands but simply by the muscular pull from the ears alone.

When you get more and more proficient, you can begin to use a slight resistance, as advocated in Exercise A of this series.

Exercise D of the Auricular Series

If you look at page 55, Diagram D, you will see that not only are you to make the pull from the ears spread farther down over the cheeks, but you are also to make the pull come from the sides of the forehead just over the outer corners of the eyebrows.

By doing this you will begin to get a tension that will draw the flesh backwards from the central point above the bridge of the nose, where the little vertical lines appear when you frown, and thus help to erase them from your brow.

Glancing again at Diagram D, you will notice that you have also got to make a pull from under the sides of the eyes and over the cheek-bones, towards the ears, and so begin to draw out the sagging lines that are apt to come there.

To accomplish all this, we must divide the exercise into two parts.

1. Sit as before with your elbows on the dressing-table and place the tips of the three middle fingers of each hand on the forehead in a line vertically just above the outer corners of the eyebrows.

Place the two thumbs on the cheek-bones slightly below the outer corners of the eyes.

Having got this position correctly, clench the teeth and draw the ears backwards and upwards.

At the same time, with the three fingers push the flesh just above the eyebrows, as if it were going backwards towards the ears, and push back the thumbs also towards the ears, so that the flesh under the eyes is pressed back with them.

Now in the same way as I have described for Exercises A, B, and C of this series, practise these movements patiently, until you can distinctly feel the pull of the muscles at the sides of the forehead, and also under the sides of the eyes.

When you have been working for some little time, try to do the exercise without the help of the hands but by the surface muscles alone.

2. Here we want to increase the pull from the ears still farther over the cheeks.

To accomplish this, place the three middle fingers of each hand vertically on either side of the face, about half an inch below the corners of the mouth.

Having got this position correctly, clench the teeth and draw up the ears and also all those parts of the cheeks over which you have already gained control.

At the same time push back the flesh on either side of the mouth by pressure from the fingers, so that it also moves up towards the lobes of the ears.

Continue to practise as for the other exercises in this series until you feel you can do the movements without the help of the hands.

Later, as you get more and more control, you can begin to use a very slight resistance, as advocated in the A, B, C exercises of this area.

Exercise E of the Auricular Series

This is simply an intensification of Exercise D.

Look at Diagram E, page 55, and you can almost see for yourself what is to be done.

You have to get the pull from the ears coming still farther forward, so that it is taken:

From right over the centre of the eyebrows, back along the forehead towards the ears.

From right under the eyes at the inner corners in a line towards the ears.

From right from the corners of the nose in a line towards the ears.

From right from the corners of the mouth in a line towards the bottoms of the ears.

From right along the jaw-bone from the centre of the chin up towards the back of the ears.

Be sure *not* to get the pull along the jaw-bone going up to the front of the ears.

Follow the lines taken by the little arrows on the diagram in Fig. 6 and you will be right.

To accomplish this exercise fully we must divide it into four parts and practise each separately, afterwards combining them as one full exercise.

1. Place the three middle fingers of each hand immediately over the eyebrows in such a way that the third fingers of each hand nearly touch over the bridge of the nose. The finger-tips should be pointing up towards the roots of the hair.

Having got this position correctly, clench the teeth. Draw back the ears and also all those parts of the cheeks and forehead over which you have already gained control.

As you do so, push back the flesh over the eyebrows with the fingers in a line towards the tops of the ears, so that *all frowning lines between the eyebrows* are erased.

Practise this patiently until you can draw back the flesh without the help of the fingers in the same way as I have already described in former exercises.

Later, as you get more and more control, you can begin to use a light resistance.

2. Place the three middle fingers of each hand just under the eyes.

Clench the teeth. Draw back the ears and also all those parts of the cheeks and forehead over which you have already

gained control. As you do so, *very gently* with the fingers draw
back the skin under the eyes in a line towards the ears.

Practise this patiently until you can feel the pull distinctly
in the muscles under the eyes. Then do the movement without
the help of the fingers, as advised in previous exercises.

You will notice that I have told you to perform this exercise
gently, as the flesh under the eyes is *very, very* delicate.

This is the movement which, if persisted with in
conjunction with No. 3 of the Third Area, will prevent sagging
skin under the eyes, because it strengthens all the small
muscles in their neighbourhood and keeps the flesh so firm
that it has no tendency to fall.

Later, when you have gained complete control, you may use
a very slight resistance when practising the movement, but
only do so gently, and be sure not to push the skin into
wrinkles in this very delicate part.

3. Place the three middle fingers of each hand on either side of
the nose, so that the third fingers come exactly at the corners
of the nostrils. All three fingers should be spaced about one
inch apart from each other, going in a line towards the ears,
with the tips pointing upwards towards the eyes.

Having got this position correctly, clench the teeth and
draw back the ears and also all those parts of the forehead,
eyelids and cheeks over which you have already gained
control.

As you do so, push back the flesh on either side of the nose
with the fingers, so that the lines between the nose and mouth
are quite erased.

Practise this patiently until you can draw back the flesh
without the help of the fingers, as in previous exercises.

Later, when you feel you have gained sufficient control, you
can begin to use a very slight resistance sometimes and so still
further increase your power.

4. Place the hands one on either side of the face, so that the

two wrists meet in the centre of the chin, the two palms cup the jaw line and the fingers spread out fan-like just behind the ears – all except the two little fingers, which should come just in front of the lobes of the ears.

Having got this position correctly, clench the teeth and draw back the ears and also all those parts of the forehead, eyelids and cheeks over which you have already gained control.

Meanwhile push back with the hands all the flesh of the jaw from the centre of the chin up along the jaw line towards the back of the ears.

Practise this patiently until you can feel the pull of the muscles drawing back the flesh. Then try to do the movement without the help of the hands, as in previous exercises.

Later, when you feel you have gained sufficient control, you can begin to use a little resistance and so still further increase your power.

Exercise F of the Auricular Series

Exercise F is designed simply to make the movements of the A, B, C, D, E Auricular Series altogether into one complete exercise, so that you do them all at the same time and thus achieve the *Great Triangular Pull* (see Diagram F, page 55).

To do so, place the hands one on either side of the face, so that the three middle fingers of each hand come just over the eyebrows, their tips pointing upwards to the roots of the hair.

Place the top part of the palms where the fingers join on to them so that they come along the cheek-bones.

The actual palms should cup the cheeks, and the lower edges of the palms where they join the wrists should lie just under the jawbone line.

Having got this position correctly, clench the teeth and pull up the ears. At the same time push up and back the whole of the sides of the face and chin in such a way that the age lines are drawn quite out.

While you are using the hands, *be sure you also use all the muscles that you have just been learning to get control over, so that it is a combined effort of the muscles and the hands.*

Don't simply push up the flesh with the hands, as that will do no good at all – in fact it will tend to stretch the skin, which at all costs we wish to avoid.

When you feel that your A, B, C, D, E, F face muscles are all pulling upwards, remove your hands and *try to keep the flesh drawn up by muscular effort alone.*

Don't lift the corners of the mouth as if you were smiling either. Make all the effort come through the ear centre. And keep the mouth as serious as you can, because a smile in this exercise simply increases the lines you are trying to draw out.

Practise this movement until you can sense all the surface muscles drawing the skin earward.

I can do this Great Triangular Pull to a point where I feel as if the A, B, C, D, E, F muscles were like tight elastic bands under my skin, all pulling upwards and backwards from the central points of the face.

Of course, the lines will reform in your skin a little from laughing and frowning and making the various expressions in which the human countenance indulges – it couldn't well be otherwise. But if you will, so to speak, *iron all lines out every day, by doing these exercises thoroughly*, they will never become very hard or unsightly, while if you have some wrinkles already deeply marked on your face, they will gradually improve.

Once you have mastered the Great Triangular Pull, it will be unnecessary to do the auricular exercises separately as I have written them down here. All you will have to do *then* is to practise the said Great Triangular Pull *for a few minutes every day.*

If, however, you *have any special lines that you wish to eradicate* it will be advisable to use whichever exercise of the A, B, C, D, E, F series seems most suitable for your purpose *in conjunction with the Great Triangular Pull.*

This chapter may have seemed very long to you, it certainly has to me! But describing the exercises in detail has been the only way to make them clearly understood.

Once you really know how to do them, they are very simple, and you needn't give any special time to them at all.

The Great Triangular Pull can be practised at any odd moment during the day for five minutes while you are reading, sewing or walking.

And this amount will be *quite* sufficient for your purpose.

Chapter Nine

Chapter Nine

Six exercises for the Fourth Area

If you look at page 19 once more, you will see that the part of the face comprised in the Fourth Area is the forehead, taken in a line from slightly above the eyebrows horizontally. This line extends round the back of the head and includes in its domain the whole scalp.

Now consider the muscles in this area.

The scalp is moved in front by a large muscle which goes up vertically over the forehead to the top of the skull, where it is met by a second which joins it to another at the back of the head.

It is these muscles which have the power to move the scalp up and down on the head. But just as ordinary civilised people have lost the knowledge of how to use the muscles of their ears, so most of them have also forgotten how to use their scalp muscles properly.

You will occasionally find a child who can move the whole of the top of the head, but in adults it is rare.

At this point, let's look and see what happens when people raise their eyebrows – in surprise, for instance. They draw up the eyebrows, and this causes the skin to go into wrinkles right across the forehead.

If you can train your scalp to move backwards simultaneously as one muscle, so that when you raise your eyebrows the whole skin of the forehead and head works upwards to a point at the back of the head, you will form no wrinkles across your brow.

The movement I advocate will be very slight – people won't be aware of it – but it will be sufficient to give free play to the eyebrows, so to speak, that they may move up and down easily without the haunting fear of wrinkles.

I'm not one of those who advocate keeping an absolutely expressionless face in order to avoid lines. Oh, no! Express what you like with your face, only learn to use your muscles in such a way that your expressions leave no ugly age lines behind them.

A mobile scalp gives a further great advantage, in addition to those already described, for it causes the blood to circulate more thoroughly in the hair roots and so lessens any tendency there may be towards baldness or greyness.

So now let's try to master the six exercises for the scalp muscles, which will do so much for the beauty of your brow and also incidentally for your hair.

No. 1. Exercise for the forehead muscles

Place the three middle fingers of each hand on the forehead, exactly along the line where the hair grows, with the finger-tips pointing upwards.

Then raise the ears slightly. As you do so push the skin under the hair-line upwards towards the top of the head.

Hold it in this position while you count 20. Then relax the pressure of the fingers, but don't remove them.

Repeat this exercise over and over again until you begin to feel a slight power of movement in the muscles under the hair-line.

Then remove the hands and try to do the same thing without their help.

It will take you a little time to achieve this, but probably not so long as it did to learn the 'ear-raising exercise', as this muscle is a big, strong fellow and soon develops his power.

No. 2. Second exercise for the forehead muscles

Place the three middle fingers of each hand about two inches *above* the hair-line, with their tips pointing upwards.

Then raise the ears slightly, and as you do so push the skin under the fingers upwards, towards the back of the head.

Hold it in this position while you count 20. Then relax the pressure of the fingers, but don't remove them.

Repeat this exercise over and over again until you begin to feel a slight power of movement in the muscles under the fingers. Then remove the hands and try to do the same thing without their help.

No. 3. Exercise for the higher part of the forehead muscles

Place the three middle fingers of each hand right on the top of the scalp with the tips pointing towards the back of the head.

Raise the ears slightly, and as you do so push the skin under the fingers backwards over the top of the head.

Hold it in this position while you count 20. Then relax the pressure of the fingers, but don't remove them.

Repeat the exercise over and over again until you begin to feel a slight power of movement in the muscles under the fingers. Then remove the hands and try to do the same thing without their help.

No. 4. Exercise for the muscles at the back of the head

Place the three middle fingers of each hand right on the back of the head in such a way that the finger-tips point downwards towards the nape of the neck.

Then raise the ears slightly, and as you do so push the skin under the fingers downwards.

Hold it in this position while you count 20. Then relax the pressure of the fingers, but don't remove them.

Repeat the exercise over and over again until you begin to feel a slight power of movement in the muscles under the fingers. Then remove the hands and try to do the same thing without their help.

No. 5. Combination exercise for all the scalp muscles

This exercise is simply a combination of the last four.

Place the two hands on the head in such a way that the bases of the palms come just above the eyebrows and the tips of the fingers point backwards over the top of the scalp.

Raise the ears slightly, and as you do so push back the whole of the flesh of the scalp with the hands.

Hold it in this position while you count 20. Then relax the pressure of the hands, but don't remove them.

Repeat this exercise over and over again until you begin to feel a slight general movement backwards in the muscles of the scalp.

Remove the hands and try to do the same thing without their help.

No. 6. Exercise for raising the eyebrows correctly

Make exactly the same movements described in the last exercise.

When you have done so raise the eyebrows in the ordinary way, as if you were surprised at something.

Meanwhile try to get the sensation that the whole skin of the forehead from the eyebrows up is moving back over the top of the head, in such a way that no lines are crinkled up across the brow.

When you can achieve this, remove your hands and try to

do the same thing without their help.

Practise this movement at odd times until it becomes second nature. You will gradually find that when you express surprise you will do so in the correct way!!

Chapter Ten

Chapter Ten

Goodbye

Well, now I think I have taught you all I know about this subject, and so I must soon lay down my pen. But before I do there are a few things I would like to add.

I have great faith in these exercises myself. If I hadn't, I shouldn't practise them every day, as I always do. But though I have faith in them, I have just *two fears*.

One fear is that the world we live in is such a busy place that few have the time or concentration to give my system a fair trial.

I can well imagine somebody buying this book, reading it and saying to herself: 'An excellent idea. It seems very practical. I shall certainly try it.'

For the first week she will do some exercises faithfully every day.

But she will see no change in a week. Oh, no! Muscles aren't built up in that time. So, because she doesn't get a quick result, she loses enthusiasm and misses two days. Then she starts again and does three days, with another break of perhaps a week.

At the end of a month of this kind of treatment she says, 'Oh! these exercises are no good – I can't see any difference in my face', and she dashes off, leaving my little book behind in a drawer – forgotten!

I also fear for another type of person.
She buys my book and proceeds faithfully to practise my

exercises three times a day. She does them *hard, hard, hard* for a month. Then she examines the result in her looking-glass.

'Hallo! What's this?' she says. 'I don't feel very certain about these exercises. I believe I look older!'

Well, candidly, I think she probably does.

For, you see, she has overdone them, and has worked off too much fat from her face and throat, and as the muscles haven't yet had time to get fully developed, her face is thinner and the skin has a slightly more drawn appearance than it had before. *It takes considerable time really to develop muscles,* whereas fat cells are easily and rapidly broken down.

Now to this woman I say: reduce the number of your exercises, and only do them once a day, *but have faith in my system and go on.*

If you stick it for six months or so, I don't think you will have any cause for complaint, because by then the muscles will really have begun to get firm, fill out the hollows and take the place of the fat which you have worked off.

Once you are convinced of the beneficial effect of these exercises, you must get into the habit of doing them for a short time every day of your life, as a matter of course, just as you clean your teeth or brush your hair, so as to keep up the muscular strength you have developed.

I would advise everyone to learn all these movements *in front of a looking-glass.*

When you have thoroughly mastered them, they can be practised at odd times. But, I repeat, they should be learnt in front of a glass. The reason is that if you learn them without watching what you are doing, you may easily acquire bad habits, such as raising one eyebrow higher than the other, or twisting up your face in such a way that you will be *making* lines instead of drawing them out.

If you are busy, with little time to spare, don't try to master all the exercises at once. That is quite against my theory. *Go very slowly.* Learn the movements of the First Area, and do them for a month, just once a day, until you know the feel of them thoroughly. Then gradually begin the exercises of the Second Area and learn those, and so on to the end of the book.

Let your slogan be, 'There must be regularity, but no hurry or rush.' You have all the years left you to practise the exercises, and the more regularly and slowly you do them the better will be the result in the long run. *If you give five minutes a day for always, it will do more permanent good than an hour a day done intermittently.*

Personally, I give ten minutes every morning before breakfast and about ten minutes, if I can spare it, in the afternoon, but I never miss the morning exercises. A beginner, however, shouldn't do more than five minutes a day at most, gradually increasing after a month or two to five minutes twice a day and so on.

The *ideal* way to get the best result from this system if you aren't in a mad rush is as follows.

Settle a time when you won't be disturbed, and then do all the exercises of the First, Second and Third Areas before your looking-glass.

When you have finished them, lie down on your bed *comfortably on your back*, with a low pillow, and in this position do the *Great Triangular Pull* of the Auricular Series for about five minutes.

Then *relax all muscular effort.* Just continue to lie on your back with your eyes closed and think pleasant thoughts for five or ten minutes – or as long as you wish.

You will then, I guarantee, look your best.

This is an excellent plan to follow before going to a party, or when you want to look specially nice.

For the very busy person there are other less perfect methods, although these, if worked at a little at a time, will also give good results.

I consider that the exercises of the First, Second and Third Areas will do a great deal of good, even if you can't master the

Auricular Series and those of the Fourth Area, but I believe that if you begin with these First, Second and Third Area movements you will, by practising them, get your deeper flesh muscles into such a firm condition that the more difficult Auricular Series of surface exercises will in time come to you quite naturally.

Well, the beauty of youth means a great deal. Therefore guard your youth and your beauty as you would guard your dearest possessions. And if this little book helps some of you to do so, I shall feel that I haven't lived quite in vain!

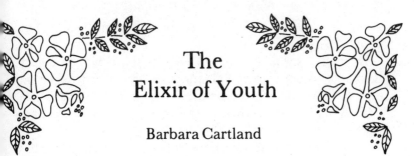

The Elixir of Youth

Barbara Cartland

Elinor Glyn, to keep her own marvellous good looks, didn't rely entirely on the beauty hints she gives in this book. From America she obtained the 'Secret of El-Zair' – an elixir of eternal youth.

For two years, at carefully repeated intervals, she carried out the prescribed treatment, which was partly mystical, partly medical. She kept a full account of her progress in a little diary, and believed that the treatment not only rejuvenated her skin, muscles and eyes, but also removed neuralgia, neuritis and rheumatism.

Whatever the exact treatment of El-Zair may have been, we now have, in the Health Movement, some products which definitely do make one 'live young'.

Ribonucleic acids

The foremost rejuvenation treatment at the moment is RNA. This is so exciting that every day I am more and more thrilled at the results of the injections.

Some years ago three outstanding scientists, Professors Watson, Crick and Clark, were awarded the Nobel Prize for research into our body cells. They discovered that cell life depends on the provision of protein and that the synthesis of such protein is controlled by DNA, using two compounds which are known as Messenger RNA and Transfer RNA.

Revitalisation, therefore, involved controlling the health of the body's RNA supply.

Eminent scientists in Russia, Germany, Hungary, Rumania, America and England have shown that when our own RNA-producing mechanism is slowing down or failing, fresh RNA introduced into the body has a *long-term stimulatory effect*.

I have taken these injections myself. The first thing that happened when I took them was that in exactly the same time that I had previously dictated 6,000 words of a novel, I now dictated 7,000 with no extra effort.

Everyone taking the injections on my advice has reported an added activity of the brain and a feeling of well-being. Elderly men rediscovered their virility. Women looked and felt younger and were altogether happier.

The course, which is expensive at the moment, consists of two injections given once a week for four weeks. But personally I think it depends on the patient's age and personal reaction. One very important finding, by Professor Dyerkerhoff, is that 'overdosage is impossible'.

For further details of RNA write to me: Barbara Cartland, Camfield Place, Hatfield, Hertfordshire.

Melbrosia

A brilliant Viennese scientist, Dr Paul Urban, was the first person to separate pollen into male and female. His Melbrosia for Men and Melbrosia Executive not only alleviate signs of old age, force away depression and fatigue and improve the intelligence, the memory and the power of concentration, but increase and restore vitality. Athletes have found that it has a miraculous effect on their endurance and staying power.

Melbrosia P.L.D. (*Pour les Dames*) has the unique attribute of enlarging a woman's breasts without her putting on fat anywhere else. So many women suffer all their life from self-

consciousness at being flat-chested, because they think it
indicates a lack of femininity in their personality. Melbrosia
P.L.D. firms the body and gives the woman who takes it a new
energy and vitality.

If she can't, for some reason, take Hormone Replacement
Treatment, which I write about next, then Melbrosia P.L.D.
will provide her with some of the hormones she needs during
the menopause.

Melbrosia for Men, Melbrosia Executive, and Melbrosia
P.L.D. are sold in most health shops or are available through
the Health and Happiness Club, Brook House, 25 High
Street, Alton, Hants.

Hormone replacement treatment

Women can remain looking young and feeling full of vitality
for ever if they take oestrogen at the outset of the menopause.
This natural substance, in the shape of Premarin, prevents the
change of life and all symptoms of it. Ninety per cent of
American women take it, which means that they don't suffer
from hot flushes, night sweats, backache, headache,
menopausal depression, or the drying up or shrinking of the
vagina which, for some women, can make intercourse painful.

Oestrogen also prevents brittle bones in older women. A
world expert on osteoporosis says: 'A fracture has never been
seen once the therapy has been properly instituted.' Dr
Wilson, the eminent New York gynaecologist, who wrote
Forever Feminine, says: 'If a man withered outside as a woman
withers *inside*, something would have to be done about it.'

After an hysterectomy Premarin is essential, as it keeps a
woman from ageing inside and out and prevents all the
irritation, nerves and frustration of encroaching age. I take
Premarin 1.25, a natural oestrogen, and I feel marvellous. A
smaller dose is 0.65.

Premarin is obtainable on a doctor's prescription. Ask him

to read *The Lancet* of 16 January 1971, page 135, where evidence is produced from four important gynaecologists that oestrogen *prevents* cancer, especially uterine cancer.

I take, as advised, one Premarin tablet a day for three weeks, and then stop a week and start again. If my breasts feel tender or prick slightly, it means I have enough oestrogen in my body, and I stop the tablets for two or three days or ask my doctor for Duphoston. Some gynaecologists recommend that this should always be taken with oestrogen. I believe it is essential to take Vitamin E with Premarin, but at different times of the day, i.e. Premarin in the morning and Vitamin E in the evening.

If your doctor won't give you H.R.T., I will give you the names of several specialists in this field. Once you have a prescription from a specialist, your local doctor is very unlikely to refuse to renew it. There are also H.R.T. clinics at hospitals everywhere.

The three natural hormones are: Premarin, Progynova and Harmogen.

The stress pill

It would be impossible for us not to realise that, with the terrible anxieties that beset us today, most adults suffer from mental strain. There are a thousand things which make men and women a prey to what we call 'stress'.

It is something which affects us both mentally and physically. Unfortunately the medical profession often has no cure but to prescribe tranquillisers, which in my opinion make people worse. I have often said that tranquillisers and sleeping pills rot the brain. In some cases, if taken indiscriminately, they reduce the patient to a psychiatric case.

For some years now I have been helping people by advising them to take three marvellous ingredients which give them energy, vitality and self-confidence. I have found that this particular combination makes people feel happy. If you are happy the world is a better place, not only for you but for everyone with whom you come in contact.

The three magical substances I have suggested are: ginseng, Vitamin E and Vitamin B6.

Now, as we all know, people are terribly casual about their health. They wouldn't think of forgetting to buy food for their lunch or supper; they would certainly not forget to provide themselves with tea for their cup at four o'clock. But they will take one of my magical ingredients and forget to take the other two, or take two and forget one of the other vital components.

I have therefore persuaded Dr Len Mervin, head of the scientific laboratory at Healthcrafts, to produce my magical formula in one capsule. This makes it perfect for men who say they will take one capsule or tablet only, and no more – and then dash off to the office!

All you have to remember is to put the capsule by your husband's place at breakfast and take your own at the same time. Then forget about your health for twenty-four hours with the knowledge that you will feel extremely well, happy and self-confident.

The stress pill, as I call it – the proper name is G.E.B. – is to my mind one of the most exciting things we have ever had in the Health Movement, and thousands of people have written to tell me so.

Ginseng

Let me tell you first about ginseng, because this is a fabulous substance which has only just come into our lives. It is fascinating to know that ginseng was first written about in China in the first century B.C. and was also mentioned in the ancient Atherva Veda in India. In 1714 Father Jartoux, a missionary for many years among the Chinese, wrote a whole book on ginseng.

The story of its discovery and all the modern applications of it are described in a fascinating book, *Ginseng* by Pamela

Dixon (Duckworth, 1978), available both in hardcover and paperback.

The Chinese consider ginseng the supreme remedy for any sort of sexual inadequacy, and the finest grades of Chinese ginseng were reputed to have the power to restore fertility, even to those who had long passed the normal child-bearing age. The Ancient Greeks spoke of it as an important ingredient in love philtres. But all this knowledge was kept in the East, and it was only about fifteen years ago, when I was in Hong Kong, that I first heard of ginseng.

It was then terribly expensive but prized, I was told, not only by the rich Chinese, but by the very poor, who saved up to buy it, as they believed it made them well and prolonged life.

Now ginseng is obtainable in all health food shops. I find it so wonderful that I can't think how we managed without it.

There are no side-effects to ginseng. I am convinced not only that it makes you feel well, but that its name, which means 'all healing', is deserved.

In the stress pill there are 400 mg of ginseng, which I find is the right amount for me to take every day. You can take as much as you like, but you have to be careful that it doesn't make you so active that you can't sleep.

Other ingredients of the stress pill

The next magical ingredient is Vitamin E, which I call the 'love, life and sex vitamin' because it supplies us with all those things, besides being a prevention and cure for the diseases of the heart. As it carries oxygen all over the body, it is excellent for the circulation. Put externally on a scar, it removes every trace of the scar in time. This shows its amazing healing qualities.

The last, very important ingredient in the stress pill is

Vitamin B6. For years it was assumed that we get all the B6 we need in our diets. But recently it has been shown that many people can be deficient in this important vitamin.

Hospital patients, who were given a diet which was adequate except for Vitamin B6, are known to have developed depression, sore mouths, lips and tongues, insomnia, extreme weakness, nervousness, dizziness, nausea and vomiting. The strangest abnormality, however, was eczema, which appeared first in the scalp and the eyebrows, around the nose and behind the ears. When Vitamin B6 was administered to them their condition quickly became normal.

Doctors now say that any woman 'on the pill' should be given B6, and they have also discovered that tantrums in children can be the result of a B6 deficiency. I have said for a long time that Vitamin B6 is the answer to what so many people call 'my nerves'.

I think that everyone who takes the stress pill in this coming year will find they look at life quite differently. Their anxiety, apprehension and fear will disappear.

G.E.B. is obtainable from all health stores or from the Health and Happiness Club.

Lecithin

In my search for the Elixir of Youth, in which I have tried a great number of products, I have always believed that lecithin is important not only for our bodies but for the brain.

In fact, as a famous nutritionist once said: 'No lecithin, no brain.'

This is something I have always remembered, because while the cells in the brain contain a large amount of lecithin, it has been calculated that the dried weight of the brain has 25 per cent lecithin – about twice the amount that is in our internal organs. The main part is used in the construction of the cells, and since we all know that our cells are continually dying and being rebuilt, a regular supply of lecithin to them is absolutely essential.

Under conditions of stress, which most people suffer from today, lecithin serves as a source of energy, and scientists suggest that this is because it activates so quickly. Lecithin has also been proved to be important in a great many other conditions.

I have found for years that Vitamin E is a marvellous help to diabetics, and a doctor who prescribed a mixture of Vitamin E and lecithin found that the insulin needs of his patients quickly decreased because of the enormous improvement in their condition.

I have also always felt that the original lecithin we have been taking, which is made from soya flour, isn't really the natural way of taking it, because the word 'lecithin' means 'yolk of egg'. When Maurice Gobley discovered lecithin in 1850 he called it after the Greek, which is *lekithos*.

Now, for the tirst time in the Health Movement, we have an egg lecithin made by Ortis. Personally, I think it is absolutely delicious. It tastes exactly like zabaglione or that delicious Dutch egg liqueur, advocat.

The first reason why lecithin was thought to be so important was that it protected men against a build-up of cholesterol in the blood vessels. We all know what happens when an elderly person gets hardening of the arteries. Therefore a wise precaution, when a man is over thirty and a woman has passed the change of life, is to take lecithin every day.

Hundreds of people die every day from coronary heart disease and a large proportion of them are men who haven't yet reached retiring age. Coronary disease accounts for more than 25 per cent of all deaths, and the figure is rising at an alarming rate. In all the industrialised nations in the Western world it is the most common cause of death, and yet fifty years ago it was comparatively rare. We all know that one of the main causes is too much cholesterol in the blood.

This is where lecithin comes in. Trials with animals have shown that lecithin fed to rabbits who were receiving large amounts of cholesterol prevented it from collecting in the blood and in the blood vessels, and also prevented hardening of the arteries.

Ortis Egg Lecithin contains honey wine – which pleased me. This is the same as the ancient mead that made our ancestors so strong and well and was the only alcoholic drink they had. Other ingredients are Royal Jelly, Vitamin E and, most important, Vitamin B6.

One unexpected result of taking egg lecithin I discovered personally. An elderly woman in my house was suffering from extreme breathlessness, which was so bad that it was almost asthmatic. The one thing that relieved it was lecithin.

Lecithin can also help you slim. It keeps the body trim and the skin beautiful, and prevents gallstones. It is also good for many skin disorders, such as psoriasis, eczema and some forms of acne which are caused by faulty food absorption.

Lecithin has been called the 'fat fighter' because it is the nutrient which has a major function of burning up fat – it does this faster than anything else – and because it keeps the fats on the move. Finally, it relieves the retention of water in the body. In fact it is a natural diuretic.

I disapprove of slimming drugs which inhibit the appetite, and diets which, if kept to for any length of time, can prove dangerous. I suggest therefore than anyone who is over-weight should maintain a sensible diet, with nothing exaggerated, and take egg lecithin twice a day before meals. Ortis supplies a small goblet which tells you the exact amount of the dose – the only difficulty is that it is so delicious that one is inclined to cheat and drink more!

To sum up, lecithin for health, for youth and for brains! It is important that *your* brain should understand this.

Ortis Egg Lecithin, Healthcrafts Lecithin capsules, and Lanes Lecigran Lecithin granules are available from all health stores.

Vitamin B15 Plus

I visited Russia recently, and just before I left England we were told of the fantastic findings about Vitamin B15. Scientists in America and Russia believe that they had perfected a miracle cure, besides finding the long-sought-after secret of eternal youth.

B15 is the extract from apricot kernels, the same substance as B17, which has been claimed as a cure for cancer.

This claim caused an uproar in the United States, where it was said that too much of it could be dangerous. But Dr Paul Buck, a respected American biochemist, says that it is completely harmless.

The Russians, I was told, were giving B15 to their athletes to improve stamina, and one of their famous professors had said that B15 would soon be 'as common as table salt in Russian homes'.

I was determined to find out for myself about this new vitamin, having always been interested in reports that in the Hunza country there was no cancer, and practically no other disease, owing to the enormous quantities of apricot kernels consumed by those who live there.

Therefore, when I was in Leningrad, I asked if I could see some of their foremost specialists who were working on B15. I was taken to the Leningrad V.M. Bekhterev Psychneurological Research Institute where I met Dr Vladilen P. Beljaev, head of the Science and Organisation Department, and Professor Yuri Geebachov, who were both working with B15. They told me that they had found that when they combined B15 with ginseng the result was fantastic.

Dr Bernard Rimland, Director of the Institute of Child Behaviour in San Diego says: 'B15 makes autistic kids more normal.'

Following my conversation in Leningrad with Dr Beljaev, the Cantassium Company have made up a vitality pill which consists of B15, ginseng, B6 and zinc.

I have found that this fully justifies all the confidence that has been placed in it, and I recommend it very strongly as a rejuvenating pill, not only for women to look beautiful but for men who are athletes or are suffering from stress.

Ginseng again

As I have written about ginseng above I will only add that it is fantastic for endurance, and that when the last American astronauts went to the moon they were told that they *had* to take it.

I find when I have extra demands on my vitality that two dessertspoonfuls of a ginseng elixir will carry me through to midnight. I take three Panax ginseng tablets every morning.

Salus-Floradix, Ginseng Elixir and Red Kooga Ginseng Elixir are available from all health stores. (And don't forget to buy a copy of the book *Ginseng* by Pamela Dixon.)

F.F. face cream

A long time ago – in 1953 – Bicknell and Prescott discovered that a number of disorders of the body were associated with a Vitamin F deficiency. According to these two scientists, Vitamin F is very important in any disease in which fat absorption is impaired. It was found to be effective against ulcers, asthma and other allergic conditions, dental cavities, acne and other skin disorders.

Finally, after an enormous amount of research it was discovered that the Vitamin F was converted in our bodies into another, far more important vitamin, Vitamin FF, which was named 6:9:12 octadecatrienoic acid. Vitamin FF is an important substance in the building up of tissues, and it is involved in many bodily processes, including structural fat development, prostaglandin production and cell function.

In simple words this vitamin is the basic life requirement and the source of youth. Vitamin FF has been put into a face cream which has an amazing effect on the skin. I am confident in time that it will remove wrinkles. It is completely free from any form of allergy, and I have found it effective even on the delicate tops of my eyelids to take away the crepeness.

It is available from all health food shops or the Health and Happiness Club.

Celaton honey moisture cream

We all need a moisturiser these days, especially in the winter when the elements play havoc with our skins and central-heating makes it dry and lined. Celaton honey moisture cream, available from all health stores or the Health and Happiness Club, both heals and rejuvenates.

Hin Yang's Phamino-4

This is a moisturiser and skin food rich in protein, amino acids, enzymes and vitamins. Particularly good for women over fifty, it is available from all health stores.

Celaton face mask

This is very new. It is just a sheet of paper impregnated with collagen. Make three holes for the eyes and nose, and put it on the face damp with water.

For older skins, damp the paper with elastin, a skin extract, and collapur, a skin fibre.

Available from Celaton Laboratories, 128 High Street, Edgware, Middlesex.

What to avoid if you don't want to age prematurely

1.   *Sedatives*, including aspirin. If you feel on edge or bad-tempered take:
   4 Vitamin B6 tablets, 100 mg each.

2.   *Sleeping Pills*. These make a woman look hideous, besides rotting the brain. If you can't sleep take:

   1 large teaspoonful of honey with
   1 dessertspoonful of cider vinegar in a tumbler of water with
   4 dolomite tablets.

You *will* sleep.

3.   *Smoking*.

4.   *Alcohol*. The worst drink, which destroys your youth and your looks, is gin. Whisky, except in small amounts, makes you dull and surly and is anti-sex. Port and red wine are bad for most people. Rum is all right, but fattening.
   The best drinks are a *small* quantity of champagne, and brandy. Moselle is all right, but hock makes one disagreeable.

5.   *White sugar* is an enemy of health and beauty.

6.   *White bread* causes diverticulitis.

7.   *Orange, grapefruit and pineapple juice* are too strong for most stomachs, and must never be taken except fresh off the tree, and only in very small amounts.

8.   *Caponised chickens, fluoridated water, any foods with artificial colourings* or containing *monosodium glutamate*.

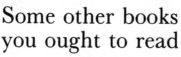

Some other books you ought to read

If you have enjoyed this book, there are others you may be interested in too. All the following are obtainable in bookshops, or in case of difficulty direct from the publisher (Duckworth, The Old Piano Factory, 43 Gloucester Crescent, London N.W.1. Tel: 01-485 3484).

FEED YOUR FACE
Dian Dincin Buchman

A complete herbal guide to health and beauty packed with fascinating information about the natural care of hair, skin, eyes, mouth and feet.

ABC OF NATURAL BEAUTY
Dian Dincin Buchman

A convenient handbook, arranged alphabetically, of all the main natural remedies for beauty problems.

GINSENG
Pamela Dixon

In the East the legendary plant ginseng has for thousands of years been regarded as a panacea, valued as an aid to long life, an aphrodisiac and a wonder-working drug. This is the first book to trace its true history from the earliest Chinese herbals to the present day, and to assess its real uses scientifically.

BELLY DANCING
Tina Hobin

The ancient art of belly dancing is coming to be recognised in the West as a skilful artform which combines health-giving exercise, graceful dance movements and a degree of exhilaration and relaxation second to none. This comprehensive manual tells you how to do it to perfection.

THE SOYBEAN GROW AND COOK BOOK
R. G. Whisker and Pamela Dixon

A staple food in the East, soybeans have recently attracted serious attention in the West as a rich source of protein. This book describes how to use and grow the soybean not as 'artificial meat' but as a delicious vegetable in its own right.

A PASSION FOR GARLIC
Penny Drinkwater and Elaine Self

Garlic is an important ingredient in many cuisines, but has been generally neglected in the Anglo-Saxon world. This unusual cookery book presents dozens of original and traditional recipes from different countries, with interesting facts and theories about its medical and culinary efficacy.